Grade

1

Name

Date of exam

GW00418904

Contents

Editor for ABRSM: Richard Jones

page

LIST A

1 **Anon.** Menuet in F: No. 6 from *Nannerl Notenbuch* — 2

2 **Joseph Haydn** (1732–1809) Andante: from Symphony No. 94 in G, Hob. I/94, second movement, arr. Alan Bullard — 3

3 **James Hook** (1746–1827) Gavotta: No. 3 from *24 Progressive Lessons*, Op. 81 — 4

LIST B

1 **Pauline Hall** Tarantella — 5

2 **Martha Mier** A Story from Long Ago: from *Romantic Sketches*, Book 1 — 6

3 **Felix Swinstead** (1880–1959) A Tender Flower — 7

LIST C

1 **Stephen C. Foster** (1826–64) Camptown Races, arr. Robin Proctor — 8

2 **Fiona Macardle** Late at Night — 9

3 **Kevin Wooding** Vampire Blues — 10

Other pieces for this grade

LIST A

4 **J. C. F. Bach** Schwaebisch in D. No. 6 from *Clavierstücke für Anfänger* (Schott/MDS)

5 **Naudot** Babiole. *Piano Progress*, Book 1, arr. Waterman and Harewood (Faber)

6 **Purcell** A Song Tune, Z. T695. No. 3 from Purcell, *Miscellaneous Keyboard Pieces* (Stainer & Bell)

LIST B

4 **Rybicki** Longing: from *I Begin to Play*, Op. 20 (PWM/MDS) or *Pianoworks Collection 1*, arr. Bullard (OUP)

†5 **Schubert** The Trout. *Simply Classics*, Grades 0–1, arr. Gritton (Faber)

6 **Schumann** Soldatenmarsch (Soldiers' March): No. 2 from *Album für die Jugend*, Op. 68 (ABRSM) also in *Schumann for Younger People* and *More Romantic Pieces for Piano*, Book 1 (ABRSM)

LIST C

4 **Bartók** Quasi adagio: No. 3 from *For Children*, Vol. 1 (Boosey & Hawkes/MDS)

5 **Janina Garścia** Allegretto: 1st movt from Sonatina in C, Op. 51 No. 1. Garścia, *Little Sonatinas* (PWM/MDS)

6 **Lajos Papp** Grasshopper: No. 15 from *22 Little Piano Pieces* (Editio Musica Budapest/FM Distribution)

† This arrangement only

First published in 2010 by ABRSM (Publishing) Ltd, a wholly owned subsidiary of ABRSM, 24 Portland Place, London W1B 1LU, United Kingdom

© 2010 by The Associated Board of the Royal Schools of Music

Music origination by Barnes Music Engraving Ltd
Cover by Økvik Design
Printed in England by Headley Brothers Ltd, The Invicta Press, Ashford, Kent

Menuet in F

No. 6 from *Nannerl Notenbuch*

Anon.

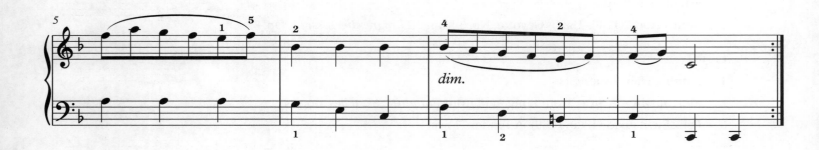

Nannerl Notenbuch Notebook for Nannerl

This piece comes from a collection that Leopold Mozart (1719–87) compiled in 1759 for his eight-year-old daughter Maria Anna, nicknamed Nannerl (sister of Wolfgang Amadeus), whom he was teaching to play the piano at that time. Crotchets might be lightly detached throughout. Slurs and dynamics are editorial suggestions only.
Source: L. Mozart: *Nannerl-Notenbuch*, 1759; original manuscript, property of the Internationale Stiftung Mozarteum, Salzburg

Reproduced from *Selected Piano Examination Pieces, 1999–2000*, edited by Richard Jones (ABRSM)

Andante

from Symphony No. 94 in G, Hob. I/94, second movement

Arranged by Alan Bullard

Joseph Haydn

The great Austrian composer Joseph Haydn (1732–1809) visited London twice during the 1790s. There the last 12 symphonies that he composed, the so-called 'London' symphonies, all received their first performance to great acclaim. The second of the 12, No. 94 in G (1791), was nicknamed the 'Surprise' Symphony soon after its first performance due to the sudden *fortissimo* chord for full orchestra that wakes up a drowsy audience during the quiet string theme of the slow movement. That theme, together with its 'surprise' in b. 16, is given here in a piano arrangement.

Gavotta

No. 3 from *24 Progressive Lessons*, Op. 81

James Hook

James Hook (1746–1827) was precociously gifted as a child. He played keyboard concertos in his native town of Norwich at the age of six and had composed a ballad opera by the age of eight. He spent most of his adult life as an organist in London.

Gavotta is Italian for 'gavotte', a dance of pastoral character in moderate duple time. In this gavotte all slurs and dynamics are editorial suggestions only.

Source: *New Guida di musica, Being a Compleat Book of Instructions for Beginners on the Piano Forte or Harpsichord…to which is added Twenty-four Progressive Lessons*, Op. 81 (London, 1796)

AB 3544

The Associated Board
of the Royal Schools of Music

This is to certify that

JACK DAVEY

was examined in

GRADE 1 PIANO

and passed

in the spring term 2012

QCF Level 1 Award (6 credits)
Graded Examination in Music Performance

Presented for examination by
MR TIMOTHY HENDER

G R Perricone
Chief Executive

ABRSM, 24 Portland Place, London W1B 1LU, United Kingdom
Registered charity no 292182

2012A/B262/3408911/0/2/L/602/4072/10/4/2012

Graded music exam

Candidate ___Jack Davey___

Presented by ___Mr Timothy Hender___

Subject ___Piano___   Grade __1__   Marks

A3 A careful account of this little dance but several 'wrong turnings' were taken today so it was extended. Small blemishes occurred periodically in notes and rhythm. An enlivened pace and lighter touch would help character.

20

30 (20)

B1 Much of the L.H. was missing from the chords unfortunately and vitality is yet to be developed here before the excitement of this whirling dance can be communicated.

18

30 (20)

C3 This was tackled with some enthusiasm and a good tempo was chosen. Co-ordination and precision were not secure initially but you found some of its character as it progressed.

24

30 (20)

Scales and arpeggios or unaccompanied traditional song

Scales were cautious in touch with several uneven moments but keys were known. Broken chords were more fluid.

16

21 (14)

Sight-reading (and transposition) or Quick Study

The key of F major was not grasped and the pulse was rather erratic. Several correct pitches however.

14

21 (14)

Aural tests

Good response to tests C and D. Timing was misnamed in test A and parts of B were also in error.

13

18 (12)

Additional comments

Some anxious moments today but a successful outcome happily achieved. Develop rhythmic control and character – with suitable tempi – as you move on.

Total	105
Maximum (Pass)	150 (100)
Pass	100
Merit	120
Distinction	130

This form records the result of an exam held on 30 03 12   Examiner code C 197

The Associated Board of the Royal Schools of Music
A company registered with limited liability in England and Wales No. 1926395   Registered as a Charity No. 292182
Registered office: 24 Portland Place, London W1B 1LU   Telephone +44 (0)20 7636 5400   Email abrsm@abrsm.ac.uk   www.abrsm.org

Tarantella

B:1

Pauline Hall

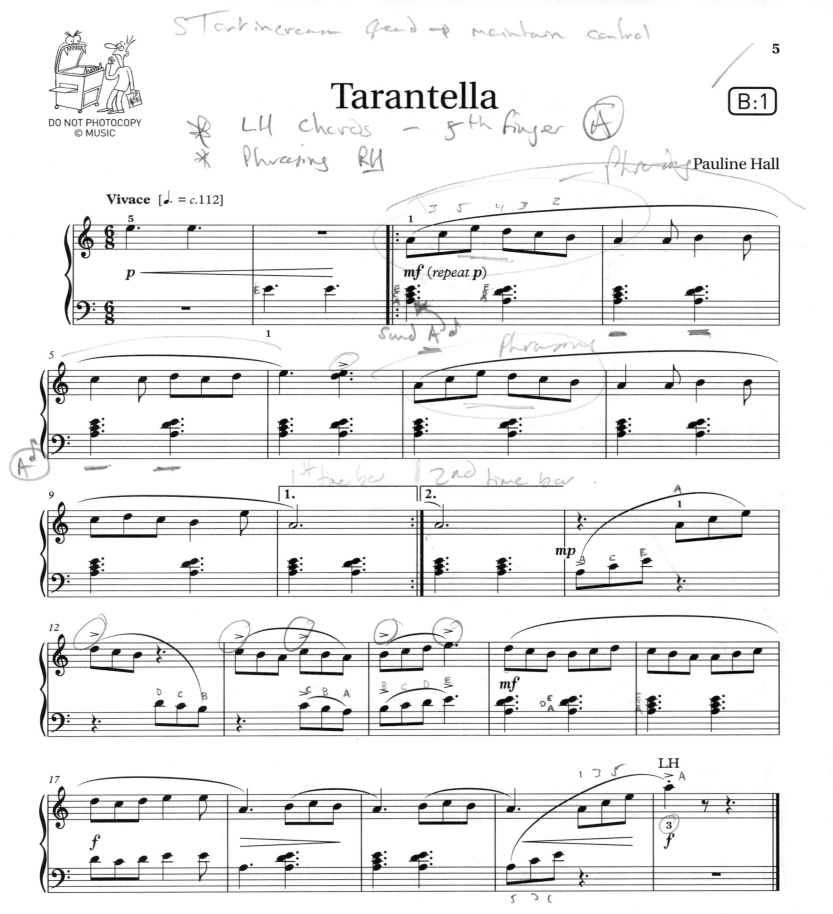

Pauline Hall studied at the Royal Academy of Music before embarking on a teaching career. It was while she was teaching in Harrogate, North Yorkshire, that she felt the need for a piano tutor that made learning fun, while progressing at the pace of her slowest learner. She started by writing little tunes in pupils' notebooks, which formed the basis of her *Tunes for Ten Fingers* and from which her Piano Time series – from which 'Tarantella' is taken – was developed.

The *tarantella* is a folk dance from southern Italy in a quick 6/8 time. Dancing it was said to cure the bite of a tarantula, but the name of the dance is in fact derived from the town of Taranto.

A Story from Long Ago

from *Romantic Sketches*, Book 1

Martha Mier

Martha Mier is a piano teacher, composer and adjudicator in Lake City, Florida. She specializes in writing educational piano music and is especially known for her popular series *Jazz, Rags & Blues* and *Romantic Impressions*. In the piece selected here, the pedalling is optional for exam purposes.

AB 3544

A Tender Flower

Felix Swinstead

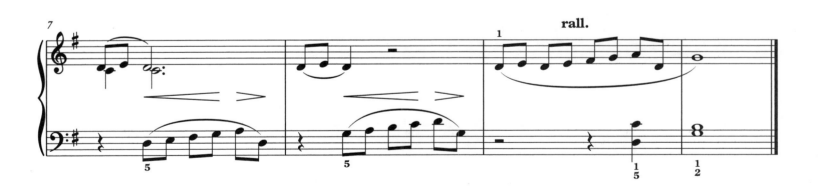

Felix Swinstead (1880–1959) was an English pianist, teacher and composer who studied at the Royal Academy of Music, where he was appointed professor of piano in 1910. Before the First World War he gave many piano recitals, both in London and in the provinces, and from 1917 he was an ABRSM examiner. Most of his published works are for the piano, and many of these were written for educational purposes.

Camptown Races

Arranged by Robin Proctor

Stephen C. Foster

The American songwriter Stephen C. Foster (1826–64), who was largely self-taught as a musician, composed about 200 songs between 1844 and 1864. About 30 of these, including the popular *Camptown Races* of 1850, are minstrel songs with choral refrains, originally sung by the celebrated Christy Minstrels. The first verse and refrain of *Camptown Races* read:

De Camptown ladies sing dis song – Doo-dah! doo-dah!
De Camptown race-track five miles long – Oh! doo-dah day!
I come down dah wid my hat caved in – Doo-dah! doo-dah!
I go back home wid a pocket full of tin – Oh! doo-dah day!

Gwine to run all night! Gwine to run all day!
I'll bet my money on de bobtail nag – Somebody bet on de bay.

The song is given here in a piano arrangement for the black keys only. For fun (outside the exam) it would be worth trying it on the white keys in G major.

© 2010 by The Associated Board of the Royal Schools of Music

Late at Night

Fiona Macardle

Fiona Macardle is a Durham-based piano teacher. As a composer of educational piano music, she has contributed to numerous volumes in OUP's Piano Time series, notably *Piano Time Jazz*, from which this piece has been selected.

Vampire Blues

Kevin Wooding

Kevin Wooding was born in Australia in 1964 and studied music there and in New Zealand. In 1987 he moved to England and currently works in Oxford as a teacher and composer. 'Vampire Blues', written in 1993, comes from *Spooky Piano Time*, edited by Pauline Hall and Kevin Wooding. The composer has written: 'You must count steadily and carefully – rests are very important, and there are lots of them. Beware of the vampire's "bite" near the end!'

— acciaccatura — very short /grace note
                     no value in time

♪.

♪ staccato.